Friends

M000276022

Photographed and hand painted by Kathleen Francour
Stories by Sylvia Seymour

Photography: © 1997 Kathleen Francour
Carefree, Arizona. All rights reserved.

ISBN: 0-7853-2121-7

PUBLICATIONS INTERNATIONAL, LTD.
7373 North Cicero Avenue
Lincolnwood, Illinois 60646

A Friend By Your Side

"I'm glad you're my friend," said Adam.

"I'm glad you're my friend, too," said Heather. "Let's go play in the park." The two children walked to the small park next to Adam's house.

Adam and Heather went to the same school. They had the same teacher. They did everything together! They were best friends. When Adam told a joke, Heather laughed the loudest. When Heather was sad, Adam would always cheer her up.

They sat on a stone wall and looked at the flowers in the park. Butterflies flitted about together.

"Look at those two butterflies," said Adam. "Do you think they are best friends, too?"

❧ · · ❧

Jesus, friend of the little children,
    Be a friend to me.
Take my hand and ever keep me
    Close to Thee.

Teach me how to grow in goodness
    Daily, as I grow.
Thou has been a child,
    And surely Thou dost know.

Never leave me nor forsake me,
    Ever be my friend,
For I need Thee from life's dawning
    To its end.

May the road rise to meet you,
may the wind be always at your back,
may the sun shine warm on your face,
the rain fall softly on your fields;
and until we meet again,
may God hold you in the palm of His hand.

Lord Jesus,
Help me never to judge another
until I have walked many miles in his shoes.

Food Tastes Better When It's Shared

Zac and Katy sat down to eat the snacks Mother had fixed for them. "Oh boy! I've got popcorn. It's my favorite," said Zac.

"I've got raisins. They're MY favorite."

"Would you like some popcorn, Katy?" Zac held out a handful of popcorn.

"Oh, yes please! Would you like some raisins?" asked Katy. She gave a handful of raisins to Zac. Soon both Zac and Katy had a tasty mixture of popcorn and raisins for a snack.

"Look what WE made," said Katy. "Mmm, it's good."

"Food tastes BETTER when it's shared!"

A friend is someone who doesn't judge.
A friend is someone who loves me for me.
A friend can play and make me happy,
but a friend also understands when I can't play.
You are my friend, Jesus.
Thank you for being my friend.

Dear friends, since God so loved us,
we also ought to love one another.

I John 4:11

I feel lonely today, Jesus.

Everyone else seems to have friends, but I don't.

Help me to know that You, Jesus Christ, are a

friend to everyone and that You are the

best friend I could ever hope for.

With You by my side, I know that I am never

truly alone.

A friend loves at all times.

Proverbs 17:17a

My Best Friend

"Mommy, who is your best friend?" Casey asked as she crawled up onto her mother's lap. Casey and her tattered teddy bear snuggled close to Mother.

"I guess your daddy is my best friend, next to Jesus."

"I have a best friend. I can always talk to Him. He helps me do the right thing. He is always with me when ever I need Him."

"That sounds like a good friend, Casey. Who is He?" Mother looked at Casey's teddy bear and smiled.

"Jesus is my best friend!" Casey hugged her teddy bear. "And Teddy is my NEXT best friend."

Lord Jesus Christ,
Teach me the ways of friendship
so that I may be a good friend
to someone who needs me,
just like You.

My friend is special to me,
Lord Jesus, please help me to
keep her in my heart until we grow old.

Dear Lord,
Make me the sort of person
who causes other people to feel happier,
whatever I feel like myself.

Thank you for my friend next door,
   And my friend across the street,
And please help me to be a friend
   To everyone I meet.

Dear Jesus,

Thank you for my friend.

I know my friend is here to

comfort me when You can't be

here Yourself.